THE MOUSE, THE BIRD AND T

THE SET TEXT

MY LIBRARY

- READ.
- INTENDING TO READ.
- HALF-READ.
- PRETEND I'VE READ.
- SAVING FOR WHEN I HAVE MORE TIME.
- WILL NEVER READ.
- PURELY FOR SHOW.
- READ, BUT CAN'T REMEMBER A SINGLE THING ABOUT IT.
- WISH I HADN'T READ.

The Snooty Bookshop by Tom Gauld • Published by Canongate Books • © 2018 Tom Gauld

MARVELLO, THE AMAZING GRAMMAR MOUSE

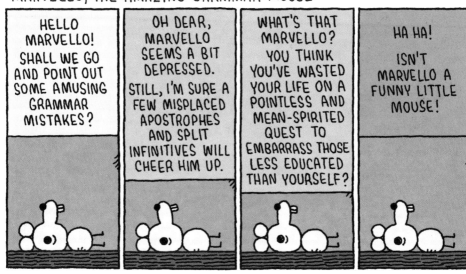

POETRY ANTHOLOGIES FOR PEOPLE WHO DON'T LIKE POEMS
LOOKS NICE ON A SHELF!
A PRETTY BOOK OF POETRY
MAINLY PICTURES!
A SHORT BOOK OF POETRY
VERY FEW POEMS!
GIVE IT AWAY!
A GIFT BOOK OF POETRY
NO NEED TO READ!

INSTITUTE OF NEOLOGISMS.

DEPARTMENT OF EVERYDAY LANGUAGE.

SOCIETY FOR THE PRESERVATION OF ANTIQUATED TERMINOLOGY.

CEMETERY OF FORGOTTEN WORDS.

THE BACKWARDS NOVEL SEEN BACKWARDS

REVIEWS OF HER BOOK LEAP OUT OF THE FIRE AND INTO THE AUTHOR'S HAND.

SHE SITS AT HER DESK AND CAREFULLY REMOVES EACH WORD FROM THE MANUSCRIPT.

UNTIL ONE DAY SHE FINDS THAT THE WHOLE THING IS GONE

SO SHE GOES FOR A WALK...

AND FORGETS HER IDEA OF WRITING A NOVEL WHERE TIME RUNS BACKWARDS.

The Snooty Bookshop by Tom Gauld • Published by Canongate Books • © 20'8 Tom Gauld

THE FAMILY OF WRITERS

THE SAINTLY MOTHER WITH AN UNGRATEFUL FAMILY: A MEMOIR

I WISH I WAS A PRINCESS: A TALE OF REGRET

THE DEAD CAT: A MYSTERY

THE STUPID DOG: A NOVEL

IDIOT: A BIOGRAPHY OF MY FATHER

LAZY: THE STORY OF TODAY'S PAMPERED YOUTH

MAGICAL ITEMS FOR FANTASY WRITERS

STAFF OF PROTECTION	HELM OF FOCUS	ELIXIR OF COURAGE	AMULET OF ATTRACTION
WARDS OFF SNOOTY CRITICS, PATRONISING REVIEWS AND INTERNET TROLLS	PUTS THE WEARER INTO A WRITING TRANCE WITHIN AN IMPREGNABLE FORCEFIELD	DISPELLS MISGIVINGS, GLOOM, BAD ADVICE AND WRITER'S BLOCK	SUMMONS MAINSTREAM ACCEPTANCE, HOLLYWOOD MONEY AND FRESH COFFEE

LITERARY BIRDS OF THE BRITISH ISLES

TREE SPARROW ENGROSSED IN A RUTH RENDELL MYSTERY

YELLOW WAGTAIL READING MARTIN AMIS ON A KINDLE

KESTREL WITH THOMAS HARDY FIRST EDITIONS

COLLARED DOVE WITH SYLVIA PLATH POEMS

PURPLE SANDPIPER ENJOYING A HILARY MANTEL NOVEL

SOME ALTERNATIVE VOTING SYSTEMS

MURDER MYSTERY

CANDIDATES ARE INVITED TO SPEND A WEEK IN AN ISOLATED COUNTRY HOUSE. VOTES ARE CAST EVERY DAY AND BY NIGHT, WHOEVER HAS THE LOWEST NUMBER OF VOTES IS MURDERED IN AN UNUSUAL MANNER.

EPIC FANTASY

CANDIDATES ARE TAKEN TO THE REALM OF DARKNESS AND IMPRISONED IN ICE. VOTERS MUST DEFEAT THE UNDEAD THEN USE THEIR BALLOT PAPERS TO MAKE A FIRE AND MELT THE ICE OF THEIR CHOSEN CANDIDATE.

MAGIC REALISM

CANDIDATES ARE TURNED INTO CATS WHO DANCE IN THE MOONLIGHT TO A FLUTE PLAYED BY A 100-YEAR-OLD WOMAN. BALLOT PAPERS ARE THROWN DOWN A WELL AND THE WINNER'S NAME APPEARS IN AN AVOCADO.

OUR DEAR, DEPARTED BOOKS...

DROPPED IN THE BATH

LENT TO AN UNRELIABLE FRIEND

ACCIDENTALLY RECYCLED WITH THE NEWSPAPERS

LEFT ON A BUS

MAULED BY A BABY

TAKEN ON AN ITALIAN HOLIDAY AND NEVER CAME BACK

MIGHT BE IN ONE OF THOSE BOXES IN THE BASEMENT

TIPS FOR GETTING YOUR NOVEL PUBLISHED DURING A SKELETON APOCALYPSE

TAKE THE INITIATIVE

PUBLISHERS RARELY READ UNSOLICITED MANUSCRIPTS BECAUSE THEY ARE TOO BUSY FIGHTING OFF MURDEROUS SKELETONS. SELF-PUBLISHING MIGHT BE YOUR BEST OPTION.

CREATE A BUZZ

WE ALL SPEND MOST OF OUR TIME IN CAVES AND CELLARS, HIDING FROM THE SKELETONS. WHY NOT TRY READING A CHAPTER OF YOUR BOOK TO THE CAPTIVE AUDIENCE?

CONSIDER YOUR AUDIENCE

THOUSANDS OF SKELETONS EMERGE THROUGH THE GATES OF HELL EVERY DAY. WITH HUMAN READERS IN DECLINE, IT MAY BE WORTH TAILORING YOUR WORK TO THE SKELETON MARKET.

HARD DAY AT THE WRITING DESK?
UNWIND WITH ONE OF OUR AUTHORS' COCKTAILS

THE
REJECTED
MANUSCRIPT

THE
MEDDLING
PUBLISHER

THE
DREADFUL
REVIEW

THE
DISAPPOINTING
SALES FIGURES

The Snooty Bookshop by Tom Gauld • Published by Canongate Books • © 2018 Tom Gauld

AN X-RAY OF MY SUITCASE

The Snooty Bookshop by Tom Gauld • Published by Canongate Books • © 2█18 Tom Gauld

The Snooty Bookshop by Tom Gauld • Published by Canongate Books • © 2018 Tom Gauld

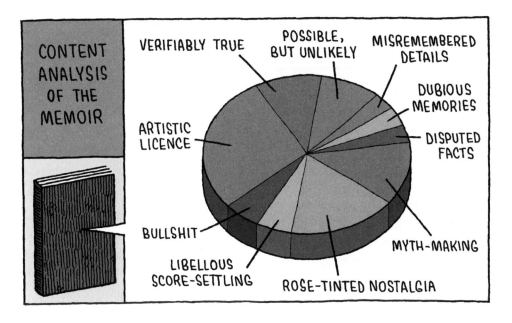

THE SLIGHTLY VAIN BUT REASONABLE QUEEN, THE MAGIC MIRROR AND THE BLOSSOMING STEP-DAUGHTER
YOUR STEP-DAUGHTER IS MORE BEAUTIFUL THAN YOU.
REALLY?
'FRAID SO.
OH WELL. THAT'S LIFE, I SUPPOSE. HAVE YOU SEEN MY EMBROIDERY?
ON THE SOFA.
THANKS.

COST BREAKDOWN OF A SLIM VOLUME OF POETRY

PRINTING
RETAILER'S CUT
SALES DEPT.
BRIBES
SLUSH FUND
DISTRIBUTION
EXCESSIVE BONUSES
CHAMPAGNE
FOCUS GROUPS
COMPANY JET
CORPORATE ESPIONAGE
POET'S ROYALTY

POET'S ROYALTY BREAKDOWN

AGENT
MANAGER
STYLIST
MANAGER'S AGENT
AGENT'S MANAGER
CHAMPAGNE
HANDMADE NOTEBOOKS
ANTIQUE QUILL PENS
MASSEUR
SUSHI CHEF
FLOWERS
ARTISANAL INK
ICE SCULPTURES

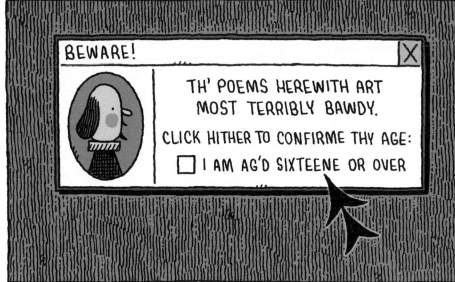

THE NINE ARCHETYPAL HEROINES

ROMANTIC

TRAGIC

MYSTERIOUS

HARD-BOILED

CYBORG

MURDEROUS LIBRARIAN

CAVEWOMAN

VICTORIAN TIME-TRAVELLER

INSECT QUEEN

BAD WRITING

A COURSE EXPLORING ALL ASPECTS OF TERRIBLE LITERATURE

BOOK YOUR PLACE NOW AND BECOME THE AWFUL WRITER YOU KNOW YOU CAN BE!

WEEK ONE

FINDING YOUR LOUSY VOICE

WEEK TWO

DEVELOPING YOUR CRUMMY IDEA

WEEK THREE

WRITING APPALLING DIALOGUE

WEEK FOUR
CREATING DREADFUL CHARACTERS

WEEK FIVE

EDITING YOUR PILE OF RUBBISH

WEEK SIX

GETTING YOUR HORRIBLE BOOK PUBLISHED

THE FOUR UNDRAMATIC PLOT STRUCTURES

I. IGNORING THE MONSTER	II. ERRONEOUS ACCUSATION	III. THE ENIGMA UNSOLVED	IV. DIMINISHING DESIRE
THE HERO IS CONFRONTED BY AN ANTAGONISTIC FORCE AND IGNORES IT UNTIL IT GOES AWAY.	THE PROTAGONIST IS ACCUSED OF WRONGDOING, BUT IT'S NOT A BIG THING AND SOON GETS SORTED OUT.	THE HEROINE IS FACED WITH A PROBLEM BUT IT'S REALLY, REALLY DIFFICULT SO SHE GIVES UP.	A MAN WANTS SOMETHING. LATER HE'S NOT SO SURE. BY SUPPERTIME HE'S FORGOTTEN ALL ABOUT IT.

THE SERIOUS ROCK CRITIC
HUMBUG!
AHA! A YOUNGSTER. STEALING MUSIC NO DOUBT.
I'M COLLABORATING ONLINE WITH MUSICIANS ALL OVER THE GLOBE TO CREATE AN ELECTRONIC SYMPHONY.
I'VE WRITTEN 32 BOOKS ABOUT LED ZEPPELIN.
I'M QUITE BUSY ACTUALLY.
MICK FLEETWOOD ONCE FELL INTO MY POND...
CAN YOU GO AWAY NOW PLEASE.

THE MANIFESTO WRITERS GET FEEDBACK FROM THE FOCUS GROUP

AIRBNB REVIEWS FOR CASTLE DRACULA

OLD-WORLD CHARM!

AS THE HOST SAYS: "THE WALLS OF MY CASTLE ARE BROKEN. THE SHADOWS ARE MANY, AND THE WIND BREATHES COLD THROUGH THE BROKEN BATTLEMENTS" BUT WE WERE ENCHANTED. THANKS COUNT!

BRING EARPLUGS!

I WAS KEPT AWAKE BY THE CONSTANT HOWLING OF WOLVES. HOST WAS UNSYMPATHETIC, JUST SAID "THE CHILDREN OF THE NIGHT. WHAT MUSIC THEY MAKE!" AND CRAWLED OUT OF THE WINDOW.

DON'T BOTHER!

MY WIFE WAS BITTEN BY SOMETHING IN THE NIGHT AND HAS BECOME AN UNDEAD MONSTROSITY WITH WANTON DESIRES AND AN UNQUENCHABLE THIRST FOR HUMAN BLOOD. ALSO, TERRIBLE WI-FI.

The Snooty Bookshop by Tom Gauld • Published by Canongate Books • © 2018 Tom Gauld